In Ring, Minster and Eternity
Lies the blessing of our poverty

THE
HUMMEL-BOOK

BY THE LATE BERTA HUMMEL

✻

POEMS AND PREFACE
BY THE LATE MARGARETE SEEMANN

✻

TRANSLATION
BY LOLA CH. EYTEL

EMIL FINK VERLAG STUTTGART
GERMANY
DISTRIBUTED IN USA AND CANADA BY SCHMID BROTHERS INC.,
BOSTON, MASS.

In order to assure the congeniality of the interpretation and to take into consideration the idiomatic pecularities of some of the following children's poems originally written in Bavarian dialect, the translator has intentionally avoided a rendering in metrical form.

Second Edition . . . February 1951

Printed by Deutsche Verlags-Anstalt, G. m. b. H., Stuttgart, Germany

May these pages reveal themselves to you as
A sky studded with gleaming stars,
A meadow filled with fragrant flowers,
A house with many sheltering chambers.

PREFACE

The following pictures represent one of the best achievements of a young German girl, Berta Hummel, but they are not her first creative attempt, as she had already published a variety of other artistic works.

Who was the artist having met with such striking success in spite of her youth? A then twenty-five year old native of Lower Bavaria endowed with a remarkable gift for rendering the feelings and troubles of a mere child as convincingly as a worshipper's fervent prayers, who was just as keenly alive to the prosaic tribulations of a little village urchin as to the divine harmony of a mystic psalm.

We encounter proofs of her talent in magazines, illustrated papers and calendars, and they never fail to impress us as a bright light filling our grateful heart with its soft radiance.

Berta Hummel took the vows at the age of twenty-five in August 1934, and lived as an inmate of the Franciscan Abbey of Siessen near Saulgau in Württemberg, Germany, till her premature end in November 1946. Her all too brief existence reminds one of a garden full of flowers expected to bloom year after year, of a tree the fruits of which are being for ever looked forward to, of a shining candle which one would like to entreat: "Do go on granting us for ever such manifestations of fervor, tenderness and devotion!" And yet did her life and her creative work not also resemble a tiny window beaming brightly in the dark? A shining window diffusing its light like sunbeams brightening our dreary existence, like the sound of happy and care-free laughter ringing again after a long silence, like the blowing away of the dust often spreading its thin veil over our souls?

The "Hummelchen" (little Bumble-bee), Berta Hummel's nickname, was born on May 21st, 1909 at Massing an der Rott in Bavaria, thus being a native of the Rottal region, just like Brother Konrad von Parzham, "the eternal Gatekeeper", canonized in 1934. Her being aware of their "common earthly home as well as of their common heavenly one" presumably prompted her to set him a monument with a painting of consummate artistic skill.

The child attended the elementary school of the Armen Schulschwestern at Massing from 1916 till 1921. Her eyes and her heart were already then much keener and more receptive than those of her schoolmates. Whatever she set eyes upon, she stored in her active young mind, constantly on the look-out for new inspirations and fresh impressions. The teacher whose pupil she had been for six consecutive

Self-portrait as a young girl

years described her as a nice little girl, cheerful and lively, yet fond of variety and diversion, an easily comprehensible trait in the character of so vivacious a child. Berta felt the inner urge to collect as many impressions as possible, no doubt a pretty arduous task. She could not afford to relax, she simply had to go on seeing and wondering and pondering uninterruptedly, although her temperamental Hummel-disposition often made it very difficult for her to concentrate her attention. How strong must her creative impulse have been already at that time, if it even succeeded in overcoming such fidgety restlessness! As soon as she was able to grasp the meaning of what she saw, she started trying to render with nimble fingers what her eager eyes had perceived.

At first, these endeavours remained secret and were kept out of sight by the shy little girl. But gradually her childish fingers gained in skill and steadiness, till time and again a classmate began to recognize her own features in a small portrait. A wave of amazement surged over the whole class. For most of the children this was a new personal experience, but for Berta Hummel it meant a significant step in her young existence. As such a stream of undescribable bliss flooded her aspiring little heart, she began to realize her prospects and to foresee her future: "Now I am able to draw, I believe I shall attain my goal, I shall become famous!"

When the ten year-old Berta stood at the blackboard

grasping an assortment of colored chalks in her frail hands, and first a tree, then a meadow and, finally, a whole landscape with birds and clouds appeared magically, then all the other pupils cheered loudly. One easily believes the teacher's statement that the fame of the youthful artist was chiefly disseminated by her enthusiastic comrades. Even the smallest tots "ordered" their portrait at the street corner. "Hummelberta, do make a drawing of me, too, please!" And the child's dream of becoming a renowned artist developed into an earnest striving after a fascinating goal.

In 1921, when twelve years old, Berta left the elementary school at Massing in order to enter the Institut der Englischen Fräulein (a Catholic Institution for the education of girls) at Simbach am Inn. When leaving some years later, she passed the final examination with flying colors, having been awarded the mark I (i. e. excellent) for her achievements in the drawing and painting courses. It became more and more apparent that the child was endowed with an exceptional talent. Consequently, her parents decided in 1927 to let her pursue her studies in Munich, the artistic metropolis. Miss Hummel was now able to enjoy the many-sided and easy-going life of this unique city. She attended the courses of the Staatliche Kunstgewerbe-Schule (State School for Applied Arts) and benefitted not only from the technical training of this institution, but she availed herself simultaneously of the various possibilities of furthering her all-round education which only such an artistic center as Munich could offer. Our Hummelchen-Bumblebee developed into a high-spirited, light-hearted and easy-going songbird. She left the lower realm of grass and meadows to ascend to the higher regions of trees and clouds. At the same time, she allowed herself to be completely engrossed by the wonderful color-symphony of the fascinating town. Theaters, movies, museums, the Oktoberfest's world-famous funfair, all kinds of social events and entertainments as well as a refined home, all contributed in offering the Hummelbird a most stimulating fare. It pecked and ate on the sly, remembering its delicate flavor and transferring these interesting experiences on paper. Berta's drawings gradually disclosed a smoother technique, a greater versatility. She realized the advantages of a bolder and stronger stroke and became aware of the numerous boundaries in which her share of the world could be encompassed. All this knowledge she enfolded in a free and receptive soul and continued to steadily improve her work.

After a period of two years, Berta Hummel apparently grew tired of this lively existence and gave up her beautiful room near the Franziskaner Kloster in order to enter the Home of the Schwestern der Heiligen Familie in the Blumenstrasse.

Her life was somewhat quieter from now on, but her cheerful disposition remained unaltered. She never changed

Visit in the convent-garden

in this respect and her high spirits characterized her work just as distinctly as her religious devoutness. In this new sphere, she also became a source of happiness for her comrades, as she always found it quite natural to please others without much ado. Moreover, her humorous paintings contributed to no small extent to the success of the Home's festivities. Her friendly and absolutely unassuming behaviour met everywhere with sincere sympathy, every one "was fond of her". Both her character and her achievements — the person and the artist — were unreservedly esteemed, and the teachers unanimously declared "There will never be a second Hummel!".

Two years later, this lively, healthy and extraordinarily talented young woman took a step which appalled many of her friends and acquaintances. Putting her professional vocation into the background, she decided to follow her inner call to take the veil. In August 1934 she entered the Franciscan Abbey at Siessen as a novice — Sister M. Innocentia.

To her numerous admirers she will nevertheless always remain "our Hummel-bumblebee", the joyful and high-spirited artist. Her name will go on evoking in our mind a vision of resplendent sunlight whenever we think of her. We may picture her standing in her garden surrounded by trees and rocks, or stroking her great Dane, looking faraway over its massive head as if conversing with St. Francis, the friend of our animal brothers. We shall remember her in the midst of her pupils, as friend, adviser, helper, mother, as well as painting her charming pictures, either humorous little scenes or masterful manifestations of her fervent visions. Her whole creative work is always characterized by a striking musical endowment and a shining radiance. Nowhere does one come across one single trait capable of causing pain or annoyance to anyone. As a child, she often gave away pieces of her parents' household, later she donated the warmth of her loving heart and the fruits of her cheerful talent.

Her versatility is positively amazing. How masterfully she manages to grasp the peculiarities of the small fry.

She thoroughly understands their various predicaments. One has only to observe the face of the little tyke running away from the frog, one positively hears his piteous yet scornful wails. Or the reverent mood of the Annunciation. How touching and wistful the "Little Fiddler", how prosaic the apple-thief and the locust-hunter. Very moving, yet devoid of any maudlin sentimentality, is the charming childishness of the Christkind to whom "an angel plays the tune rehearsed in heaven by cherubs", and the Advent-child cautiously carrying a lighted candle. What a tremendous difference between these cute little figures and the treacherous cruelty of the old witch! Berta Hummel depicts her kids just as they run about in their native village with loose pants repeatedly mended and far too large for their small owner, with scrawny pigtails, untidy stockings and clumsy shoes — yet all of them crowned by large, wide-open questioning eyes. She prefers her mites to frantically clutch a few mangled grass-blades in their chubby fists rather than to let them hold a dainty bunch of fresh flowers, because she absolutely wants to show them exactly as she has picked them out of their small everyday-life, always naive, original and thoroughly un-affected. That is why they all make such a smug impression. One simply can't help joining in their carefree-laughter, one fully understands their tears and their prayers, and one implicitly believes every single word they utter. All these pictures carry one back to one's own childhood.

Besides these embodiments of simple and childish humanity, one encounters other works of an absolutely different character such as "Brother Konrad", the "Madonna in red" (first picture), the "Corpus Christi Day", the infant with the bumblebee, the pair at the wayside-shrine. One cannot help being deeply impressed by such overwhelming loftiness.

Berta Hummel's dream of long ago has been fulfilled, she has become an artist of acknowledged renown. Unfortunately, the further development of her career has found an abrupt and tragic end inasmuch as she passed away after a severe illness on November 6th, 1946. *)

The memory of the "Hummelchen" — our little bumblebee — will nevertheless go on living forever in her artistic work, this source of cheer, spiritual elation and contemplative thoughts. We are badly in need of such assistance in the midst of the misery and despondency of the present time. We want it to build up our moral strength again. We also need it to help us to relax and to learn again what our ill-fated world has forgotten,

> to laugh heartily,
> to pray fervently,
> to love devotedly.

Berta Hummel's artistic inheritance will forever remain our best teacher.

*) Notice of the publisher.

Carry your candle with care,
My child!
The wind is waiting,
The wind is waiting
To blow it out.

But the Holy Child
Sees your candle's light,
And, aware of the danger,
Follows your march.
Follows your march
Through the Advent-night
Towards the star so bright.

A bundle of straw is your cradle
And candle-light is your sun.
Your big blue eyes resemble
An unfathomable well.

Child, close those starry eyes of yours,
For what I see therein
Burns like fire and glows like the night
And shines as red as blood.

Don't try to think. Listen to me
And don't mind if I weep.
For you I am playing
The tune of sacred love
Which angels are rehearsing
In Heaven above.

If you will wander with me towards Bethlehem
And stand in front of the crib,
Your soul should be wearing
New shoes, stainless white.
A candle you must be holding
With resplendent light,
And a garland,
Woven by cherubs,
You should also wear
In your golden hair.

And your little heart should be
Full of warmest love,
As the blessed Saviour-Child,
Finding it so meek and mild,
Might choose it as shelter.

An alien chord runs invisible fingers
Over the quivering strings of Thy melodious lute,
Wrapped in dreams like a heart, still and mute.

Thou layest in God's sheltering hands
Both Thy life and the glad tiding.
At His omnipotent bidding
An angel opens the gate to the sacred realm,
While Glory everlasting climbs the resplendent steps
In awed silence,

And lifts the Sea of Darkness
On outstretched arms
Towards the coming ages, now maturing.

A solemn bound unites Earth and Heaven
When Thy Holy Command ascends the sky.

Through gloomy streets, through cold and wind
Mary carries her precious burden.
Has no one a safe refuge to offer,
Or a warm bed for the tired mother
From distant Nazareth?

Only a stable in a lonely field,
Small and bare,
Shelters the tired wanderers.
There the mother, with humble heart,
Gratefully cradles the world's Saviour
In the straw of the crib.

The oxen hold their breath and dare not move
And stare with wonder-filled eyes
Into the sleeping infant's face.
Overwhelmed by their small guest's
Exalted loftiness,
They even forget food and drink.

Fraught with disaster, the air is laden
With the burden of the heavy distance,
With the laments of the mothers and the tears in the sand.
The moon roams aimlessly accross the dark land,
Picking young lives like small stars.

Gardens must perish that one single flower —
Christ's own blossom — be cruelly destroyed.
God sees the purple flood. He lifts His hand,
Removing the tender bud from the demented land.

He wakes the sleepers, turning the angel's tidings
Into dark-hued cloak and sheltering refuge,
And calling the trembling stars
Away from crimson streets and mounting deluge
Into a glorious full-blown Eternity.

22

Sleep, my darling, go to sleep soon,
That the grass swaying in the meadow,
That the pebbles gleaming under the willows
May not sing for you their mournful tune.

Sleep, my darling, go to sleep soon...
I will pray each single birdie:
"Keep still, do not wake him!
Do not tell him one hour too soon
That thorns and nettles will hurt him."

Sleep, my darling, go to sleep soon...

Five wounds piercing my Lord,
Five crimson gates,
Five bleeding stars
Crowning His death.

Five times given away
To the henchman
For our redemption.
Five huts and five beds
For shelter and rest.

Five quests and five calls,
Five mournful greetings.
Five purple steps
For my feet to climb.

Incline, Thou seven-flamed God,
Thy radiant countenance
To this afflicted earth,
That the blaze of reviving faith
May kindle the smouldering flicker
In our despondent hearts...

Burn, Thou seven-flamed God,
All our doubts to smoke and ashes,
That our soul may be delivered
From ailments, woe and misery
Through Thy everlasting Mercy...

Spread, Thou seven-flamed God,
The shield of Thy resplendent cloak
Ov'r Thy children's longing faces,
That those kneeling at the heavenly source
May quench their thirst in Thy eternal Grace...

25

The flowers drew themselves up high
To embroider Mary's cloak
With blossoms, leaves and graceful stalks.

Each bud an angel, the tiniest stood alone,
Quite hidden by a heavy stone.

A birdie spied it. And as it was the purest,
And the quietest and the poorest,
He lifted it to the Altar for the Holy Child.

When Mary took it in her hand, it got a golden heart,
When Jesus' fingers touched it gently,
It became a star shining brightly
In the sky.

Thou hast burst the narrow bounds of human vision,
Thy house's dome rises above the distant horizon.
Thy praise swells with the voice of every living being.
The air rings with "Hosanna!" psalms o'er vale and mount.

Waving cornfields drink the coming splendor,
Roots' fingers shape already the monstrance.
In the soil seeds pray: "Oh bread, our brother,
Eternal flesh and blood dyed Thy seclusion red".

Grass and stones are silently praying,
So are future harvests and crops.
The earth's invocations are framing
The sublime creations of the Lord.

27

Humbly have I tended the herds.
I have been a reverent servant.

I was the nest sheltering the shining dove of the Lord, the nest
cradling the radiant purity of
the Holy Mother.

I was the heavy brown hand over the boards of time.
My fingers were the sickles cutting the bread for the Child Eternal.

My plane rushed over the planks, murmuring prayers.
My hammer drove in the nails and struck my heart.

The logs on the tables took, mysteriously, the shape of crosses,
And the song of my saw sounded husky from repressed tears.

My tools were like corn and like barley. They served to feed us.
Earth-like were my thoughts and could be ploughed like soil.

But the clock in my heart harkened to the voice of the Infinite.

I have sheltered the Child of Eternity unter the tent of my stillness.

I have guarded the God of my soul like the heart of my heart.

Behold the handmaid of the
Lord! The Infinite Being's
eternal servant . . .

I have lain at His feet, but
He hath raised my soul to
the everlasting minster.

Through the brightness of the One who gathers milleniums like shining stars, a lasting miracle hath come to pass in the shadow of
my heart.

I went to the well and drew water. My jug reflected the sky's glory.
I bent over the wheel and span my son's coat.

I bowed my head to the earth and shuddered as the clay glowed red.

I lifted the skies from my pails to mould the vaulted dome of Thy soul.

I bleached the linen and cut the seamless garment for the emperor's
warriors.

I prostrated myself on the ground; both knees did I bend, and I kissed
the earth's holy purple.

I kissed the precious blood of my Saviour, ere it was.

The Lamb of the world hath been born to Thee and me in the harmony
of a triple chord of holy words:

ECCE, ANCILLA DOMINI

29

HL BRUDER KONRAD

A trunk stands somewhere on rustic soil, plain and rugged, like other trees growing in arid earth.

Thou towerest above the peaks of our mountains, a symbol of exalted humility,
Thou standest besides burning candles upon the altars of our churches, an eternal gate-keeper.

What has carved Thee out of the wood of Thy poverty, out of the dull existence in Thy home-country?

It was the cheerful and implicit belief that Thou wouldst meet HIM in every stuttering lip,

In every Ave-bead of Thy cowl's cordon;

That Thou wouldst follow HIM across cell and hall,

On every step a greeting, with every stride a look,

Ever blossoming side by side, ever filled with the song of HIS nearness.

The petty things of this earth have appeased the hunger of Thy soul, as Thou hast meant them to be but a vessel for a Holy draught.

A trunk stood somewhere on rustic soil.

Now it blazes as a radiant star besides a resplendent Deity.

Thou, our brother!

I am the shepherd. My pastures stretch away to the remotest bounds of eternity.

All living beings breathe under the cover of my love.

I trace my steps through every maze like a straight thread, and thrust my fingers in every thorny hedge as in rank grass.

My shoulders are strong to carry my frightened lambs,
My blood warmeth their chilly shelter.

I set out to harvest with the call of my longing.
All the wounded and the sick I bring home

Across the ridges of the mountains, through the blaze of the wilderness and over the embers under my feet.

Lamb of my flock! Behold! I am here to seek Thee.
Thou part of my heart, I am here to love Thee.

Thou human vessel, I am here to elevate Thee through the exalted flames of my fire, till Thou becomest a fragment of the Infinite.

— — — — — — — — — — — — — — — — — — —

— — — — — — — — — — — — — — — — — — —

Who art Thou, O Lord . . .?

I am the Good Shepherd.

We are a pair of songbirds,
In father's fence we are nestin'.
There we begin to tend our herds
Early every mornin'.
The Lord on the Cross is our good friend.
He knows we are comin', but never dawdlin'.

Brother Johnnie takes his flute and plays Him
He's blowin' and fingerin'   a tune.
Just like a grown man.
I keep twitterin' and chirpin'
As well as I can,
And I spread pretty flowers at the feet of the
                                              Cross.

The lambkins are grazin'. The trees are swayin'.
We jodel and warble, and then we go home.
The mountains are blazin'. The Lord finds it pleasin'.
He smiles down on us, saying "Much obliged and thank you!"
Just like me and you
Always do.

Heavenly Mother,
Isn't your baby too heavy
Up there?
I'll carry it awhile
Up and down in the meadow
For you.

Johnnie'll chase butterflies
While I'll fondle it
Gently,
And when you are a bit rested
I'll return it
Safely.

The birdies will wonder,
The blossoms will smell sweetly
Down here.
Do let me hold your baby,
And don't be afraid
To trust me,
Mind you!

Mary and Joseph are standing
At the Holy Gate,
The Jesus-Child, beaming,
Resting at their side.
A dove, pure and white,
Softly cooes,
And flutters across
His small toes.

Your glossy throat, o blessed bird,
Pours forth the voice of the whole world.

Now that the voice of the trees cannot reach you anymore,
And you believe no longer that days are like ringing bells,
You lay outstretched on your last couch
At the bottom of steep, dark steps,
O guardian angel child!

I need fear no longer for that frail life of yours —
Where you are waiting now, one must suffer alone —
Yet I may hover round you, like a foamy down,
To spread a golden ray of the distant radiance
From across the world's border

On the narrow grave where your sweet young limbs
Rest, rigid and fragile;
To spread a golden ray of the distant radiance
As a last wide cloak to wrap around your soul
When it shall rise to cross the earth's
Ultimate boundary.

35

MADONNA WITH THE BLUE CLOAK

What is the golden crown to you,
Adorning your tresses?
Holding the Holy Child,
You feel already blessed.

You unfurl slowly your blue cloak
With silent, smiling eyes. It holds
Flower, beast and human heart
All gathered in its folds.

You are the homestead, warm and bright,
And our grief you have blessed.
I know you have kept the fire alight
For the least of your guests,
Dear Mother, even for me.

"Who is approaching our door
With such an uproar
Rending the air?"

"We are the three angel-kids!
We just want to find out
How you are faring."

"Don't stop, please, move on!
We are poor and life is hard,
Bare is our home and dark our heart."

"That's why we want you to come along.
Follow us right now into the fairest land.
Offer all those we meet a friendly hand,
Laugh and be merry
And praise God's glory!"

"What a sad and mournful tune
You are playing,
Little fiddler!"

"It sang itself into my heart
While I was plodding
Along these dreary streets."

"But how can a child's toy express
Such soul-stirring grief,
Little minstrel?"

"I am not playing a fiddle,
I am playing on a human heart."

"And why must you play
Such sad songs on a heart,
Little fiddler?"

"Hearts would for ever remain silent,
If I did not strike their chords,
As overwhelming sorrow is mute and still!"

"Begone, begone! You unknown musician!
Your melody is too depressing."

"How could it sound glad and merry,
If it means such boundless misery?"

"Hands off! Stranger, You are choking me!
Confound your awful melody!
Stop your playing or I'll chase you away
By setting my dogs at your heels!"

The weary little minstrel
Slowly leaves the hostile house,
While the sobbing of his fiddle
Is drowned in the streets' noise.

If ever in his melody there flutters a faint smile,
He'll play it over and over again across many a mile,
And hang it over the thresholds as he passes along,
While far away still lingers the echo of his song.

"What a sad and mournful tune
You are playing,
Little fiddler!"

Two little figures I can spy,
Standing irresolute and shy
At the border of the meadow
And hiding in the blue shadow
Of the big pine.

Pussykin, go on purring...
Look how hard they are staring!
They had better take heed
Or they'll never succeed
In finding their way home.

You might get into trouble,
You imprudent couple!
Yet it's not too late
To escape your fate.
Beware, beware!

If I only knew
What I should do!
I'd like to be a mouse
And nibble at that house.

Its walls are made of cookies,
Its window-panes of jellies.
Say, should we run away
Or had we better stay?

I am hankering for some candy
And my tummy feels so empty . . .
Come on! Who cares?
If gingerbread grows in the wood,
It might as well do ME some good.

41

The news has not yet got abroad —
And that's to be deplored —
That Tommy started on a trip
Around the big wide world.

Great strides he is taking,
As big as his boots allow.
As a present for Dad he'll get
Half of that big wide world yet.

Say, how long will he be gone?
The answer is a heavy sigh . . .
If only he did not miss his Mom
So hard during the night!

I'd love to kiss your little woolly snout.
Mayn't I?
As long as I tend the herd you'll be mine,
Won't you?

Don't tell them how close you are to my heart,
Because they would just laugh at me
                                    and feel smart.
You see?

And that would hurt me so that I'd have to cry.
Believe me,
A hard punishment for a kiss on your little woolly snout.

You won't tell, lambkin?
Say you won't!

43

I'd love to bring you the whole world,
If I could!
And you'd give me a dime for it.
You sure would!

I'd just squeeze the whole sky
Into my basket,
And I'd spread it in your room
As a present.

But the sky and the earth
We can't move,
So you'll just get these cookies
With our love!

May your life be as fair as my hair,   And shouldn't that be sufficient,
As lively as my heartbeat,   Just look into our eyes.
And as bright as the light   There you are sure to find
Of a birthday-candle!   What you think you are missing:

Regular "Happy birthday" wishes
Which I failed to learn by heart,
'cause you might just as well
Read them in our eyes.

Here is a letter I have written
And some flowers I have picked
In the garden for you,
As today is your birthday.

My heart is racing wildly,
And I feel that every tree
And every birdie looks at me.
I am ashamed and I am afraid . . .

But the rhymes I should have
Learned by heart
To congratulate you with,
I simply can't remember.

You know how I feel, don't you?
And I think we shouldn't show
And the others shouldn't know
That my heart loves you so dearly.

One has quite forgotten what Mummy
said:
"Run to the baker and bring six crisp
rolls,
But hurry! Tea's ready!"

And now?...

One squats in the hearth's flick'ring light
With the Seven Dwarfs and Snow
White ...
One must follow from dusk to dawn
One's enchanted brother who is now a
fawn ...
One has to ride the big brown Bear
With Rosie, when he leaves his lair...
One simply must rescue Hans and Gretel

From the wiles of the nasty old witch,
As she wants to devour that imprudent
pair
To the very last lock of their hair...
One has to call each kid by name —
That's easy, as they are so tame —
And to stare at Old Granny
In the Bad Wolf's belly...

But now to the baker. Let's hurry
In a flurry to get these rolls for tea!

Mummy dear, listen! Just one more
minute,
That wicked old Queen hasn't ended
her visit

And I simply can't leave yet..."

47

Have you ever heard the tinkling
Of the small golden bell
Ringing in a child's heart
Like a shimmering flood,
Till every drop of blood
Throbs from sheer delight?

It sounds so holy that we feel like kneeling
And kissing the glittering ripple gleaming
In its shining eyes.

Look at the small golden crown
Hidden in the tangled curls
Of even the shyest little head,
While in every pair of eyes
Slender candles stand waiting
Like long-stemmed white flowers.

No screen dims their radiance,
No shadow darkens their brilliance.
They sprout and bloom and glow
From the wonders of their hearts.

Have you ever heard the tinkling
Of a small golden bell
Ringing in a child's heart?

It sounds so holy that we feel like kneeling
And kissing the glittering ripple gleaming
In its shining eyes.

Dear Lord, O dear Lord!
Do shoo it away!
I am so awfully afraid,
I simply can't say.

Isn't the meadow large enough?
Why must it bother me?
Do lend me a hand,
And you'll get repaid
For your kind aid

With the largest
And the prettiest
And the loveliest
Bouquet.
O.K.?

50

Why are you threatening me,
You long-legged feller?
You'd better be off
As quick as you can.
Scram!

And don't you dare to show
Your face here again or I'll blow
Your brains out.
See my gun,
You bum?
One doesn't swoop down
On a hunter's man
Without proper warning.

Begone, I say!
And be quick
About it . . .
Have I perhaps ever hurt you?
And who do you think I am?
Don't you take me for a ruffian,
'cause I am a decent man.
Yea, I am!

51

Stitches, stitches, stitches
To cast and knit and purl,
To increase or knit together
Till my head is in a whirl.

These panties, warm and woolly,
Are a gift for brother Billy.
But the yarn won't slip
And the stitches will stick.
Mommy says they really look like
A pair of old stove-pipes.

It's all very well for her to say so
But her sight is failing already,
Don't you know!

Look!
What queer things happened in this book
Overnight!

Yesterday
Bill and John were fightin',
And Bill got a lickin'
On the last page.

And it all took place
In the dark,
Overnight!

And today?
The battle is raging,
And John gets the beating
On page number one.

Fancy what queer things
Happen in a book
Overnight!

Clear out, I say! Right now!
Get out of our meadow!
Did I ever do you any harm?
You'd better leave our grass alone,
And you just wait till I call Mom!

You'd like to gulp me down
Like a worm.
Pop and Mom! Do please come over
As fast as you ever can,
And bring your flails and scythes along . . .

I just can't stay up here so long
'cause this fence is awful hard,
And down there this beastly creature
Has a jaw like the deepest cave.
I am slipping! I am tottering
On the brink of an early grave!!!

Not the tiniest little bit
Did I bite off that sour apple!
You can find it in the grass below.
But now let me go!
Down I must come! Home I must run!

Dear old tree, do me a favor:
Shoot with your apples green and red
That snarling cur right through the head,
And kill it for a little while,
Till I make my escape.

If you wake him afterwards, it's O.K. with me,
As long as you let me reach my home safely.
But you'll never catch me
Climbing an apple-tree
For the rest of my days.

All good scholars
Learn their 3 R's,
Rain or shine . . .
Don't you see the books I carry?
So long! I have got to hurry.
I'd rather be wet than lazy!

The sun is burning in the sky,
And my stockings are all awry,
And I'm quite alone.
But I'm not afraid, mind you,
As I'll soon be grown up, too.

All these flowers I am picking
For that sweet Mummy o' mine.
In my heart her dear face is smiling
Because she 's sure to like them fine!

Goosie, Goosie Gander!
Don't you dare to pull my hair
Or to tear my frock!
Mind, I am big enough
To dust your white jacket
With a stick!

Watch me swing it
As high as the sky,
To give you a sound spanking
In spite of your hissing.

Goosie, Goosie Gander!
Are there only three of you?
You'd better bring over
Every Goosie-bird
From yonder patch of clover,
Nay, from the whole world!

So keep out of trouble
By being sensible . . .
Pick quarrels with frogs
But not with people.

58

Stop wriggling
And kicking
And spluttering
And sniffing,
And hand me sponge and soap . . .
I'll have to scrub you
And to dip you
Till you simply shine
Like a new dime.
Should people, seeing you so grimy,
Think you are a regular piggy?
You are my daughter, keep that in mind!
Candy instead of soap?
Yea, that would suit you . . .
Where would the world be coming to
If every kid would feel like you?

There we are! I have just posted it...
Dear mailbox, do keep a sharp eye
On the angel who will forward it
To the heavenly house of dear Santa Claus.
I've written it quite without aid,
That's why I am rather afraid.
It looks a bit cramped,
In spite of my pains.
But my next letter
Will be much better!
There goes my Christmas-list...
Good-bye!

60